IN THE FOOTSTEPS OF TIME –
GEOLOGY AND LANDSCAPE OF CUCKMERE VALLEY AND DOWNS.

By Monty Larkin
Illustration and design by Gabrielle Vinyard

Ulmus Books

First published 2006 by
Ulmus Books
The Tower House, Isfield
Uckfield , East Sussex
TN22 5UQ

© Text, Monty Larkin
© Illustrations and Cover, Gabrielle Vinyard

ISBN   0-9553368-0-5   978-0-9553368-0-5

Printed and bound in England by Tansleys Printers, Seaford, East Sussex.

Dedicated to Rachel, for her support and encouragement
and to Esme my mother

CONTENTS

PREFACE

This book, is rooted in a lifetime's interest in the subjects of rocks, countryside and the myriad of plants and animals that inhabit it. I have also, always been drawn to that cocktail which forms the agricultural industry: open countryside, farm livestock, vernacular architecture and machinery. For a significant part of my working life I was involved in the management of the Seven Sisters Country Park and the neighbouring Seaford Head Local Nature Reserve, leading to a career which I hope, has assisted in bridging the gulf that used to exist (and to some degree still exists), between the ethical, good husbandry of the landscape with its biodiversity and the wresting of food production within it. Over the past half century, these two elements have been riven apart by modern technology, after centuries of co-existence.

I would like to take this opportunity to thank the numerous sources that I have called upon in putting this book together, many of which are listed in the bibliography. I hope this book will open many more eyes to the countless partially hidden facets of our countryside, here in this corner of Sussex. I have often likened the landscape to an old, much used artist's canvas, where glimpses of previous works tantalisingly show through.

I would also like to thank Jim Berwick without whose stimulus, the seeds of this book might never have been sown. To Ann Murray of the Seven Sisters Country Park for requesting this work and for guiding and goading me into producing it! Special thanks are also due to Gabrielle Vinyard for delivering the artwork whilst attending to all the other calls upon her superb talent.

Monty Larkin

SAFETY FIRST.

A few words of warning: beware that chalk cliffs are notorious for giving way; do not stand within close proximity of the cliff edge. If venturing below the cliffs, check out the times of high and low water so ensuring you are able to return to safety well before high tide. Advise a friend or family of your expected return to dry land and ring them when you have reached it. If available, wear a hard safety hat and if possible walk some 50 metres out from the base of the cliffs to avoid falling small debris. Do not venture below the cliffs for some weeks if there has been any significant spells of rainfall or frost.

INTRODUCTION

The purpose of this book is to provide a readable, in-depth source of knowledge on the geology (rocks) and topography (landscape) of the area centred on the Cuckmere Valley in the county of East Sussex. The hope is that this book may possibly engender greater interest in geology and the spectacular scenery and wildlife that is still to be found in this busy corner of England. The text concentrates on an area broadly bound by Eastbourne, Hailsham, Lewes and Newhaven, with limited reference to features outside those margins. For all that follows, be it natural history or the exploits and struggles of Man, they are moulded by processes which began many millions of years ago and which continue, albeit slowly to our eyes, to the present time. It is written at an intermediate level for country lovers, students and all those with an enquiring mind. It is not intended as a substitute for the standard reference books and sources on the subject.

The layout of the book attempts to keep to the principle of a 'timeline,' presenting processes and events in chronological order but inevitably, this principle has frequently to suffer in order to present facts in a readable order and to avoid repetition. Time spans are generally given as millions of years 'before present', this abbreviated to 'B.P.' in the text. The book begins with the area's basic geology starting with it's main constituent – chalk, followed by the lesser components: enquiring into their origin, structure and development into today's landscape. This is followed by chapters on key periods and landscape forms. Key terms are highlighted in bold type where they first arise; where further facts are provided in numbered text boxes, this is indicated. At the rear of the book is a list of further reading.

To place the area within a wider context, the focus of this book, is seated within a long spine of hills known as the South Downs. They in turn are part of the English southern chalk uplands which stretch in excess of one hundred miles (160kms), south-eastwards from the great chalk expanse of Salisbury Plain. To the east, lie the marshlands of Pevensey Levels, formed of deep deposits of sand, silt and clay. To the north, rise the gentle ridges of the Low Weald, formed of soft clays and sandstones. Beyond, rises the High Weald, composed of various sandstones and mudstones, forming an area of high ground intersected by steep, narrow valleys. Both the Low and High Weald contain significant amounts of woodland.

The undoubted 'stars' of the geological formations are the white chalk cliffs between Eastbourne and Brighton resulting from the creation of the English Channel, the most spectacular and unspoilt section being the sheer, towering cliffs, along the coast between Cuckmere Haven and Beachy Head. Landward, the lofty, smooth humpback lines of the South Downs escarpment cascades across the expanse of the Weald, reaching westward into Hampshire...

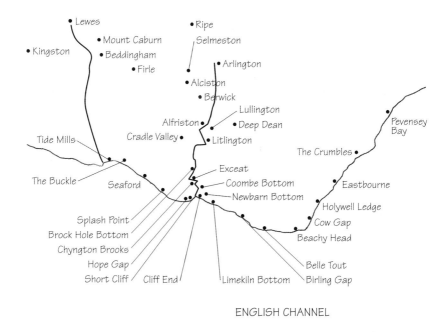

ENGLISH CHANNEL

Figure no.1 Locations Map.

PART 1 - IN THE FOOTSTEPS OF TIME

CHAPTER 1
Foundations Of The Landscape

All the rocks and deposits that occur within this area from the most recent valley deposits down to the Jurassic Beds, are classified as **Sedimentary Rocks** (Text Box No. 1). These are composed of generally fine debris and material created by the erosion and breakdown of older rocks by water, wind or ice. These sediments were then generally deposited on the beds of shallow seas where, over great spans of time, they accumulated to great thicknesses, eventually hardening into new forms of rock. At a later stage, these areas were uplifted creating new land; the process then, beginning afresh. There are no 'ancient,' volcanic or extruded rocks within the upper geology of this region.

Text Box No. 1. SEDIMENTARY ROCKS are made up of sediment and pieces of pre-existing rocks (and former plant and animal remains). Pieces of rock are loosened by weathering, (mainly involving the agents of water, wind, frost and ice), then transported to a marine basin or shallow sea where the sediment settles, eventually becoming compacted and cemented together and forming sedimentary rock. Rocks may have particles ranging in size from microscopic clay to boulders. Terminology is based on the size of their particles. The smallest grains are referred to as clay; then silt followed by sand. Grains that are larger than 2 mm are termed pebbles. Shale is rock predominantly made of clay; siltstone is made up of silt-sized grains. Sandstone is made of sand-sized particles, and conglomerate is made of pebbles surrounded by a matrix of sand or mud. Rock deposits made mostly of animal shells may form limestone-type rock or flint.

CHALK   With the commencement of a major phase of subsidence, came the formation of the great **Chalk** (Text Box No. 3) deposits that led to the formation of the chalk uplands of Southern England: the South Downs, North Downs, Salisbury Plain etc. These were formed between 100 and 65 million years B.P., during the latter part of the geological period known as the **Cretaceous Period** (Text Box No. 2). (Table No. 1). Deposition of the material which was to

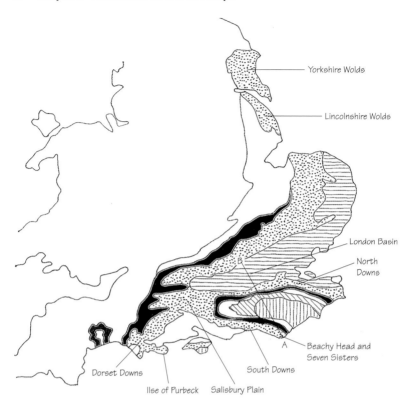

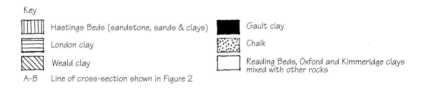

Figure no.2 Map of Geology of SE England.

make up the Chalk, took place in a warm, comparatively shallow sea over a period of many millions of years. It should be remembered, that at that time, this region's area of the Earth's crust lay far closer to the equator – the British Isles are, to this day, still moving north (Figure No. 3). With relatively less land mass worldwide, lower amounts of sediment were being transported into the seas by river systems, making these seas particularly clear, thus creating very favourable conditions for many forms of marine life.

Cenozoic Era (65 mya to today)	Quaternary (1.8 mya to today) Holocene (10,000 years to today) Pliestocene (1.8 mya to 10,000 years) Tertiary (65 to 1.8 mya) Pliocene (5.3 to 1.8 mya) Miocene (23.8 to 5.3 mya) Oligocene (33.7 to 23.8 mya) Eocene (54.8 to 33.7 mya) Paleocene (65 to 54.8 mya)
Mesozoic Era (248 to 65 mya)	Cretaceous (144 to 65 mya) Jurassic (206 to 144 mya)

Table no.1 Geological Timescale.

Text Box No. 2. THE CRETACEOUS PERIOD takes its name from the Latin 'creta', meaning literally Cretan earth: chalk. This was a period when the earth's sea level was possibly hundreds of metres higher, (the highest levels that have ever existed), creating large areas of shallow sea. It was preceded by the Jurassic Period, of which, the Purbeck Beds are locally exposed in several deeply incised valleys within the High Weald. Mean global temperatures during the Cretaceous were between 10–15 degrees C. higher than those of today – a super greenhouse scenario with large amounts of the greenhouse gases, carbon dioxide and sulphur dioxide and no polar ice caps. Sea temperatures were also considerably warmer than those of today. The Cretaceous Period began some 142-144 million years B.P. and lasted for between 77 and 79 million years, ending with a cataclysmic specie extinction episode some 65 million years B.P. This was possibly due to two events, a meteor crashing in to what is now Mexico and/or massive volcanic activity in part of what is today, India. (The demise of the dinosaurs had already occurred).

Cretaceous Earth differed markedly in other respects from the world we recognise today; girdling the equator was one vast ocean. Today's Africa, South America, Australia and Antarctica once formed an immense continent while North America, Europe and Asia formed another. Vast tracts of forest existed worldwide; flowering plants were just beginning to make an appearance while many crustaceans and reptiles bore a remarkably similar appearance to those of today.

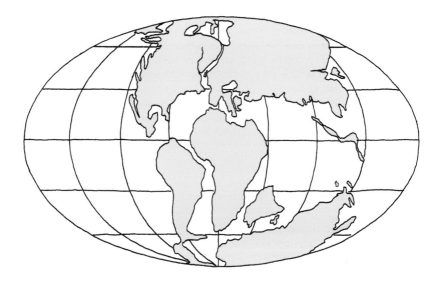

Figure no.3.1 Position of British Isles in Cretaceous Period.

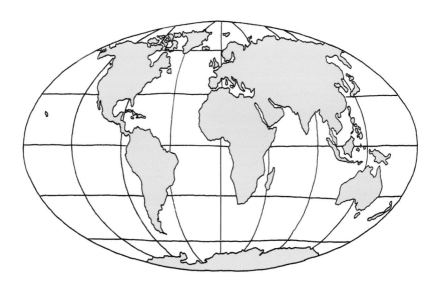

Figure no.3.2 Position of British Isles in the present day.

Text Box No. 3. CHALK: the definition as used in the British Geological Survey's Rock Classification, Volume 3 is: "The term chalk should only be used to describe limestones which are friable and porous." It is a relatively soft, white limestone composed primarily of calcium carbonate (CaCO3), reaching a purity of over 95 per cent in its upper levels, or strata. In terms of the earth's Carbon Cycle (Figure No. 4), Chalk locks away a significant proportion of the Earth's total carbon dioxide. However, current trends of increased absorption of carbon dioxide could lead to an increase in the acidity of the oceans, so reducing their ability to absorb this gas and so contribute to further climate change.

The main constituent parts of Chalk are of an organic origin: first, **Coccoliths** (Text Box No. 4), calcareous platelets secreted by microscopic marine plankton known as coccolithophores. Secondly, a slightly coarser material composed of shell debris from the protozoan (single-celled animal organisms) group, the **Foraminifera** (Text Box No. 4). Both of these life forms thrived in the warm, clear seas of the Cretaceous and are still to this day important members of the marine environment. Within this finer material were embedded sponges, sea urchins, bivalve molluscs and shrimps, evidence of which can be found as fossils within the Chalk today.

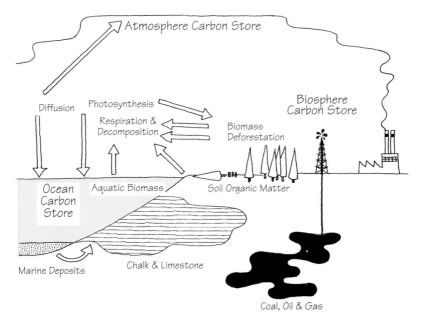

Figure no.4 The Carbon Cycle.

Text Box No. 4. COCCOLITHS are microscopic calcareous platelets in the order of 10 microns in diameter (100 per millimetre), secreted by coccolithophores – microscopic organisms which are classified as algae, being able to use sunlight to photosynthesise, but with some having animal characteristics. The platelets overlap and interlock to create variously shaped protective spheres and could number from one to hundreds of platelets per organism, the platelets being shed throughout the organism's life.

FORAMINIFERA are protozoa which have an often spherical shell with numerous openings through which they fed with thread-like extensions and which also enable them to propel themselves. Research on their fossil remains has helped establish knowledge of sea temperatures for that period.

During the Cretaceous Period, a huge amount of calcareous ooze was deposited by the remains of these organisms beneath the warm seas. With compression caused by its own ever increasing thickness, pressure from the sea above together with chemical processes, this ooze eventually solidified into Chalk rock. After the erosion of a significant proportion of the upper Chalk deposit over the intervening millions of years, there is still at the present time, in the region of up to 360 metres (1,180 feet) of Chalk remaining. The proportion of fine to coarse materials composing the Chalk varies, giving different characteristics to the various **Strata**, (the term given to the different layers or beds/bedding planes of rock).

Chalk is classified into two main divisions in Britain: those of a Southern province and those of a Northern province; in Sussex, we are only concerned with the former (Table No. 2). These are further divided into the **Grey Chalk Subgroup** formally known as Lower Chalk and the upper **White Chalk Subgroup**, formerly known as the Middle Chalk and Upper Chalk. These subgroups are in turn further divided, with seven recognisable strata composing the White Chalk Subgroup. On first sight, these strata appear similar but differ by subtle degrees in their constituent parts: the presence or not of impurities such as marls (clays), or the frequency or type of flint contained. These characteristics often extend over large geographical areas with some of the marls originating from ash clouds created by distant volcanic activity.

A few of the more notable Chalk exposures are: at the base of the cliffs just east of Beachy Head (access gained via Cow Gap steps), the lowest strata of the Chalk may be picked out opposite Head Ledge (grid ref: TV 594955), some of which contain high levels of marl. About 500 metres east of Beachy Head lighthouse it may be possible to see Melbourn Rock, the lowest strata of the Holywell Nodular Chalk

Former names	Current strata names	Local names
Upper Chalk		Studland Chalk Member
	Portsdown Chalk Formation	
	Culver Chalk Formation	Spetisbury Chalk Formation
		Tarrant Chalk Member
	Newhaven Chalk Formation	
	Seaford Chalk Formation	Dover Chalk Rock (North Downs)
	Lewes Nodular Chalk Formation	
Middle Chalk	New Pit Chalk Formation	
	Holywell Nodular Chalk Formation	Plenus Marls Member or Melbourn Rock
Lower Chalk	Zig Zag Chalk Formation	Glauconitic Marl Member or Falling Sands Member

Table no.2 Chalk Strata.

Formation, a hard, creamish-coloured rock which can reach up to 4.6 metres in thickness. Along the steep backdrop of the Downs - the **Escarpment**, it frequently forms a discernable 'bench' or terrace as seen along the Litlington to Wilmington road, above and south-east of Milton Street (grid ref: TQ 536037), or the rise along the A26 at Itford Farm south of Beddingham (grid ref: TQ433054). The New Pit Chalk, named after the disused quarry situated south-east of Lewes (grid ref: TQ 427090), forms the highest strata of the former Middle Chalk Formation, recognized as a firm, flaky but blocky sequence with few fossils and flints but with significant thin marl seams, and reaching 50 – 60 metres in thickness). An easily observable exposure of this rises alongside the A26 road west of Ranscombe Farm (grid ref: TQ 435087). The Lewes Chalk (60 – 65 metres thick), the lowest strata of the former Upper Chalk Formation, consists of a hard, nodular, often pale-yellow stained chalk, with significant and regular seams of nodular flint and marls. The Seven Sisters are formed from the Seaford Chalk Member (65 – 70 metres thick) and consists of soft to firm, pure white chalk with well developed and regularly spaced seams of flint, some of which form almost continuous layers along the cliff face. Examples of localised, comparatively hard beds of chalk, are the reefs running out from Flagstaff Point (grid ref: TV 537965) and The Mares, extending south of Hope Gap (grid ref: TV 511971).

FLINT   Incorporated within the White Chalk Subgroup are varying amounts of the mineral **Flint** (Text Box No. 5), a very hard grey to almost black rock, it being in fact, one of the hardest of the common minerals.

Text Box No. 5. *The definition of FLINT as used in the British Geological Survey's Rock Classification, Volume 3 is: "flint - a nodular form of grey/black chert [silica]. This term is restricted to nodules of chert present in Cretaceous chalk." It is composed of the very widespread mineral silica (silicon dioxide, SiO2).*

It occurs within Chalk as nodules, or as tabular sheets located parallel with the bedding plane or strata, of the Chalk. Flint was formed after the deposition of the Chalk as a result of surface water percolating down through the Chalk, carrying silica in a soluble form from the fossils of siliceous sponges and micro-animals and then being restructured. The silica was often attracted to organic remains: bivalves, sea urchins, sponges, they being encapsulated and forming flint nodules; elsewhere it can develop within the former burrows once created by invertebrates.

In its nodular form, flint is very often covered with a whitish cortex or outer layer composed of a porous layer so fine that light is scattered and so appears whitish. When exposed, on the seashore or within certain soils, flint becomes stained by iron minerals and commonly takes on a brown-tan tint. Flint breaks into angular often curved shards which can be extremely sharp, a property that was not missed by early man.

Between Seaford and east towards Beachy Head, the Seaford Formation, part of the White Chalk Subgroup dominates. Here, the flint content is of the order of 2.5%, but increases to 3.5% at Seaford Head itself. Westwards of Newhaven, the protected cliff frontage is developed in the Newhaven and Culver Formations, also of the White Chalk Subgroup, which has an estimated flint content of 1.5%.

One other mineral that occurs within the Chalk locally and can often be found below the cliffs, is **Marcasite**. It occurs as heavy, dark rusty-brown knobbly nodules, varying in size from marble size up to perhaps 125mm. (5 inches) in diameter. It is composed of iron sulphide (FeS_2), and when freshly broken apart, reveals a mass of brassy or golden coloured crystals radiating from the centre of the nodule. They are often referred to as 'fools gold,' or thought to be meteorites or 'thunder-bolts.'

UPPER GREENSAND   **Upper Greensand** is so-called on account of the presence of grains of a green phosphatic mineral called glauconite and contains numerous fossils. It was deposited under rather shallower conditions, near to shore between some 120 and 100 million years B.P. when shallow seas inundated the landmasses once more. It is exposed only sparingly in the cliffs and as scattered boulders on the foreshore adjacent to Head Ledge (grid ref: TV 594954), where it overlays the next formation, the Gault Clay. Just to the east at Eastbourne, it creates the Holywell Ledge which forms a large lagoon at low tide, known as The Pound, off the western promenade. In West Sussex it forms a noticeable ridge running along below the Downs. In the past, Upper Greensand was quarried in the Eastbourne area, being used as a building material and can be observed in older buildings: local churches, Exceat House (adjacent to the Country Park Centre) and Church Farmhouse, Litlington. As Eastbourne developed during the Victorian period it was also used extensively as a material for boundary walls and landscaping.

GAULT CLAY   By contrast, the rock formation immediately beneath the Chalk in most of this area, the fine grained **Gault Clay**, has only minute spaces between its particles. This prevents water from passing through it because of surface tension. Gault Clay consists of a stiff, greyish clay deposited in a calm, fairly deep-water marine environment during the early Cretaceous period some 110 – 97 million years B.P and is contemporary in age to Lower Greensand. Gault Clay often contains numerous phosphatic nodules and may also contain sand as well as small grains of the mineral glauconite. It yields abundant marine fossils, including ammonites, belemnites and bivalves, sharing some of the same fossils as Upper Greensand. Locally, it forms a low ridge several kilometres to the north of the Downs, including the base of the Arlington Reservoir (grid ref: TQ 530074). Between Cow Gap and Beachy Head, massive landslips are observable, having occurred as a result of groundwater causing the overlying Upper Greensand and Chalk to slip or rotate across the surface of the underlying impervious Gault Clay. Head Ledge, the rock shelf running out to sea is composed of this formation.

LOWER GREENSAND   Inter mixed within the above mentioned ridge are small pockets of **Lower Greensand**. Exposures of this sediment only occur in several abandoned sand pits in the vicinity of the villages of Ripe and Selmeston. In West Sussex, this strata broadens out to form a significant ridge including Blackdown near Haslemere, which at 280 metres (918 feet) is the highest point in the county of Sussex and visible from hereabouts.

WEALD CLAY   The **Weald Clay** lies next within the sequence, forming a broad tract of low lying landscape and consists mainly of grey coloured clays and silty clays, laid down in a variety of shallow water conditions. Narrow bands of sands and ironstone also occur within the strata and locally, thin beds of Large Paludina Limestone or 'Sussex Marble', composed largely of freshwater gastropods or molluscs. This stone was used in the past for ornamental work, hearths, doorsteps and fonts. Weald Clay has and is still to some extent, worked for brick clay.

All clays, as they are relatively soft, are easily eroded by water; this leads to clay country often being low-lying without any significantly higher land and because of the impervious qualities of clay, there is a profusion of small watercourses.

Finally, beneath the Weald Clay lie the remaining strata of the Wealden rock series that make up the landscape of south-east England: Tunbridge Wells Sand, Wadhurst Clay (once heavily quarried by the iron industry), Ashdown Beds and lastly, the Purbeck Beds, laid down in excess of 140 million years B.P. beneath a large brackish-water lagoon, connecting with a sea to the south.

CHAPTER 2
Dawn Of The Sussex Landscape

The deposition of the Chalk ended some 65 million years B.P. when an upward movement commenced across a large area, leading to the formation of what today is north-west Europe; this new land surface would have experienced sub-tropical conditions. This process arose from the collision between the African continental plate and the Eurasian plate, a train of events that also heaved up The Alps and Pyrenees. Closer to home, the effects of the collision upon the rock formations of what are today south-east England, led to **Folding** - the bending or buckling of previously horizontal rock strata, often leading to the creation of **Anticlines** (Text Box No. 6), or upward movements, the major example here being the **Wealden Dome** (Figure No. 5) and **Synclines** (Text Box No. 6), downward movements.

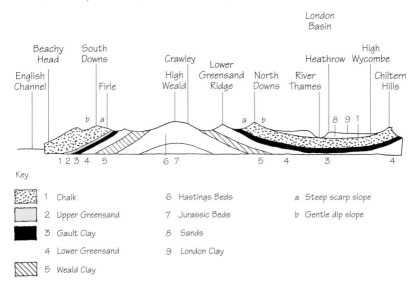

Figure no.5 Cross-section through the Weald, Wealden Dome.

At a more local level, there are examples of both these features adjacent to one another. The Kingston – Beddingham anticline, lies beneath the two villages of the same name, spanning the Ouse valley south of Lewes. Part of this feature is the two hillocks rising from the valley floor, known as Upper and Lower Rise consisting of uplifted Chalk and Gault Clay. Nearby, is the Mount Caburn syncline, causing the rock strata of the Lewes Downs, to be lower than adjacent similar strata and therefore having survived, the effects of erosion. Another effect of this collision was the tilting of rock strata and the creation of **Dip Slopes**. In the case of the Chalk, the Dip Slope causes the strata to slope towards the south-west with progressively older Chalk strata exposed as one heads northward.

Text Box No. 6. ANTICLINES; with these, a formation of stratified rocks is raised into a broad arching dome so that the strata, or layers, slope down on both sides from a common crest. With SYNCLINES a downward movement of stratified rocks takes place, creating in cross section, a saucer or trough shaped vale.

This uplift process and the ending of Chalk deposition marked the end of the Cretaceous Period, and the dawn of the so called **Tertiary Period** (Text Box No. 7), which lasted until some 2.5 million years B.P. (Figure No. 6). During this period, land surfaces were elevated, planed off and then re-submerged by the sea, on possibly two separate occasions. During these marine inundations, only the highest parts of what is today south-east England stood above the waves. With the first retreat of the sea away from these 'wealden islands' some 50 million years B.P., the river systems that formed flowed seaward with an east-west orientation. However, following the close of a second inundation, the original drainage pattern was superseded by river systems that flowed across the freshly planed land surface, southward towards a rudimentary **English Channel** and northward toward an embryonic **River Thames**. It was during the latter part of the Tertiary Period, possibly some 2 to 2.5 million years B.P. that the **Cuckmere River** was born. During most of the intervening two million years, the Cuckmere has carved out the dramatic and beautiful valley that we admire today.

At Short Cliff (grid ref: TV 511973) to the west of Cuckmere Haven, thin bands of sand, gravel and rounded flint pebbles - often cemented together, can be observed. This is a marine deposit that was laid down during one of the marine inundations of the Chalk landscape during the Tertiary Period, and is classified as part of the

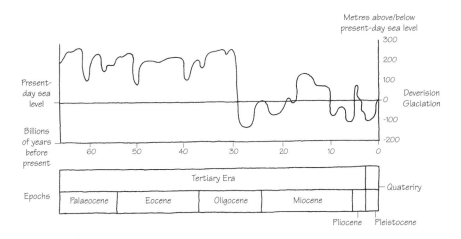

Figure no.6 Tertiary Eras changes of sea level. Approx. metres above or below sea level..

Reading Formation (Text Box No. 8). On the north facing slope of the Seaford Head golf course (grid ref: TV 496983) and on Chyngton Farm, there are several small pockets of another Tertiary deposit, the **Woolwich Beds**, consisting of sand deposits. These relatively thin additional deposits resting on top of solid bedrocks are termed **Superficial** or **Drift Deposits**.

> *Text Box No. 7. The beginning of the TERTIARY PERIOD is widely accepted as 65 million years B.P., and is regarded by various researchers to have ended between 2.5 and 1.64 million years B.P. The term Tertiary was first introduced in 1810 to describe the strata above the Chalk in the Paris region, and was subdivided into five epochs. The fact that Tertiary faunas and floras are essentially modern in aspect has made the task of interpreting evidence considerably easier than for earlier periods of geological time.*

Due to the erosive action of water and ice during the Tertiary, a significant amount of the relatively softer (relative to the Chalk), central part of the Wealden Dome was eroded away, with only the lower strata remaining. Today, these remaining rock strata of the central dome form a sequence of crests and ridges of alternating sandstone, sand and clay deposits as exhibited across the High Weald. Overall, the Wealden Dome consists of a series of concentric horseshoe-like ridges or deposits of successively younger rocks, the Chalk being the youngest.

Text Box No. 8. During a period spanning some 5 million years following the end of the Cretaceous Period, marine conditions were to return, depositing significant amounts of red and orange coloured clays beneath shallow seas and coastal lagoons, referred to as READING FORMATIONS. They are referred to as the Reading Formations or Beds because they are particularly well-developed around the town of Reading in Berkshire.

The Chalk strata were eroded away by this process fairly early during the Tertiary Period assisted by the fact that one of the properties of rainwater is that it is mildly acidic. This is because Chalk is composed almost entirely of calcium carbonate which is soluble on contact with acid. During more recent times, Chalk has been eroded in the order of 75mm (3 inches) with the passage of every one thousand years since prehistoric times; there is still remaining today in the region of up to some 360 metres (1,180 feet) of Chalk. Much of today's Chalk scenery of the South Downs is formed by a generally gentle, south facing Dip Slope, (north facing in the case of the North Downs). As this erosive action cut away outwards from the central part of the dome, only the lower, outer margins of the relatively harder Chalk were to remain, these today forming the North and South Downs – the outer rims of the Wealden Dome. An outcome of this process has been the creation a prominent steep-faced ridge, an **Escarpment** or scarpslope, which forms one of the most endearing landscape features for visitors to the Sussex. Another familiar feature of the Downs, are the long sweeping **Dry Valleys** which dissect them, and give the Downs that air of mysticism. Often referred to within their name as 'Bottoms,' these valleys were initially formed by streams at a time when the water table within the Chalk was far higher than that of today. They are often indicative of unseen features within the Chalk, as in the case of Newbarn Bottom at Exceat (grid ref: TV 528988), which follows a **Fault** (a fracture within the Chalk resulting in loss of rock continuity on either side of it). During the passage of time, the slightly acidic nature of rainwater together with its erosive action, have conspired to exploit these weaknesses within the rock.

Chalk is 20-40% porous, that is, the structure of Chalk rock allows water to drain to some degree down through its structure. Most groundwater flow however, is down through cracks, joints and Faults within the Chalk. With the impermeable Gault Clay largely forming the next rock formation beneath, Chalk can hold substantial amounts of water within its formation, an important attribute for the supply of water to man.

Escarpment of the South Downs at Firle Beacon.

> *Text Box No. 9. RENDZINA is a term used to describe friable shallow soils over-lying Chalk, consisting of a dark or black humus-rich surface layer which grades through a to a lighter brown hillwash soil. It contains small pellets of Chalk and developed in situ from the decay of organic material (humus) over the past 10,000 years. The origin of the word Rendzina has a complex history; Polish scientists began using the name for soils formed in highly calcareous materials.*

In contrast to the true Chalk soils, overlying parts of the Downs are substantial deposits of the Drift Deposit, **Clay with Flint** which forms a relatively heavy, water impermeable deposit, capping the free-draining Chalk beneath. Clay with Flint is considered to be comprised of the altered remains of former Tertiary Period deposits. When exposed during ploughing operations or during excavations, it has a distinctive ochre colour and contains a high proportion of fractured flint, as opposed to the whitish chalky soils, or the dark blackish-brown, **Rendzina** (Text Box No. 9) soil. Also dating from this period are **Sarsen Stones**, which occur occasionally on the Downs and are predominantly comprised of sandstone. A number of these large stones may be observed in the village of Alfriston, having been placed around the streets. Also to be found occasionally are conglomerates, rocks composed of Tertiary sediments cemented together some 55-61 million years B.P. A large boulder of this material may be seen south-east of Foxhole on the Country Park (grid ref: TV 527981).

CHAPTER 3
The Ice Ages

During the Tertiary and Quaternary periods (see Table 1), a succession of **Ice Ages** (Text Box No. 10) affected the Earth's climate. Europe has been subjected to at least three major periods of glacial or arctic-like conditions during the last 270,000 years alone. During these periods, vast amounts of water were locked away in the form of glaciers, ice sheets and snow-fields, causing the world's **Sea Level** to fall dramatically in comparison with present day levels. There were no actual ice fields south of the River Thames; sea pack ice however, would have existed in any neighbouring seas.

As these periodic falls in sea level progressed, the sea floors adjacent to land masses became dry land causing river systems to become greatly extended. The gradient, or slope of the existing river systems also increased together with their erosive power, this process, referred to as **Fluvial Incision** working upstream with its cutting edge termed a 'knickpoint', (Figure No. 7). Thus, during the cool, brief summers, rivers steadily cut their channels and catchment areas significantly deeper across a tundra-like landscape. In turn, the Cuckmere and Ouse were tributaries of a **Seine/Solent** river system which flowed westwards along the centre of the present day English Channel, meeting the then existing coastline far to the west between Cornwall and Brittany.

The earliest firm evidence of relative sea-level change along the present East Sussex coastline is the presence of a buried inter-glacial **Raised Beach** and adjacent cliff-line, created when the sea level was once higher than that of today. This is clearly exposed at Black Rock (Brighton Marina) and extends westwards beneath more recent sediments. The base of the rock platform has a maximum elevation of 8.5 metres above O.D. (ordnance datum - mean sea level). The superficial material present is evidently a product of cold climatic conditions during the succeeding **Devensian Glaciation**. (Text Box No. 10).

Text Box No. 10. An ICE AGE is a period experiencing a long-term downturn in the temperature of the Earth's climate, resulting in an expansion of polar sea ice, continental ice sheets and mountain glaciers. Between ice ages, there are multi-million year periods of more temperate climate. The severe cold periods are termed 'glaciations or glacial periods' with the warmer periods referred to as 'inter-glacials.' The last suite of ice ages (there have been a further four periods of ice ages in the distant past), began some 35-40 million years B.P. with the growth of an ice sheet in Antarctica, but intensified some 2.5 million years B.P. with the spread of extensive ice sheets over the European, Asian and North American continents, interspersed by the warmer inter-glacial periods.

During the last few million years, these glacial periods have occurred at around 120,000-year frequencies. The last glacial period was the Devensian Glaciation, which lasted some 60,000 years and ending about 10,800 years B.P. Some authorities consider that currently, we are only in a warmer inter-glacial period! The timing of ice ages throughout geological history is, in part, controlled by the position of the continental plates upon the surface of the earth. When landmasses are concentrated near the polar regions, there is an increased chance for snow and ice to accumulate. Small changes in solar energy can tip the balance between summers in which the winter snow mass completely melts and summers in which the winter snow persists until the following winter. Due to the positions of Greenland, Antarctica, and the northern portions of Europe, Asia, and North America within the polar regions, the earth today is considered prone to ice age glaciations.

The cause of ice ages remains controversial for both the large-scale ice age periods and the smaller ebb and flow of glacial and inter-glacial periods within an ice age. The general consensus is that it is a combination of at least three different factors: atmospheric composition (particularly the ratio of CO_2 and methane), changes in the Earth's orbit around the Sun known as Milankovitch cycles and the arrangement of the continents. Man induced global warming is now a further consideration entering into the equation.

During the last glacial interlude the Devensian, sea-level fell by at least 100 metres (325 feet). On today's seabed, several steeper gradients have been identified: off Beachy Head, one has been locatedsome 14 kms out, and may represent a Quaternary low sea-level cliff line, while another submerged former cliff-line has also been located some 6km out.

Much of the inshore seabed is fairly featureless, with Quaternary river valleys now infilled by subsequent sedimentation. However, a buried extension of the River Cuckmere has been located some 5 to 7 km southwards of the modern coastline. Unlike most other former valley sections along the eastern English Channel, this is only partially filled with sediment and therefore readily discernible from sea bed

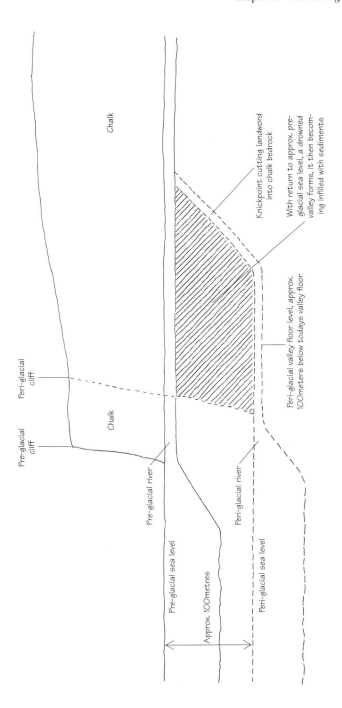

Chalk

Knickpoint cutting landword into chalk bedrock

With return to approx. pre-glacial sea level, a drowned valley forms, it then becoming infilled with sediments

Peri-glacial valley floor level, approx. 100meters below todays valley floor

Peri-glacial cliff

Chalk

Pre-glacial cliff

Pre-glacial river

Peri-glacial river

Pre-glacial sea level

Approx. 100metres

Peri-glacial sea level

Peri-glacial river

Figure no.7 Process of Fluvial Incision showing pre and ost Ice Age features

surveys, suggesting a contemporary mean sea-level 50 to 60 metres below present levels.

The Chalk bedrock floor at the mouth of the Cuckmere lies at about 25 metres below O.D., declining upstream to 13.1 metres below O.D. at Exceat Bridge. Various researchers therefore suggest that, allowing for seaward extension of valleys at gradients of between 2 and 4 metres per km, sea-level was approximately 35 metres below O.D. some 10,000 to 10,500 years B.P. Rates of cliff recession have been calculated for the past 200 years which would locate the coastline at this time some 6-12kms seaward of its modern position. In the Ouse valley, the Chalk bedrock lies at 29.6 metres below O.D. at Newhaven and at 12.2 metres below O.D. at Lewes.

Text Box No. 11. SOLIFLUCTION is the process whereby large amounts of chalk rubble, flint and water slump or slip downhill, resembling a huge spillage of cold porridge. This is due to meltwater accumulating faster than it can drain away because of the underlying impervious permafrost. Once temperate conditions had returned, normal spring action could have modified some of these coombes. During the Roman period, the water table within the Chalk was substantially higher than that of today.

The topography of the downland landscape is very much a product of the **Peri-glacial** period (conditions, processes and landforms associated with cold non-glacial environments, often associated with permafrost), that prevailed during the last re-advancement of those arctic conditions. The cold climatic conditions of the Devensian Glaciation, promoted severe freeze-thaw weathering accompanied by the mass movement of material due to the process of **Solifluction** (Text Box No. 11), down and along pre-existing Chalk valleys.

Solidified accumulations of this soliflucted material, termed **Coombe Deposits** (Text Box No. 12) including **Coombe Rock**, within the now Dry valleys is clearly visible along several coastline sections, where it has been exposed by cliff-line retreat. Even during the brief summers the permafrost lay only a few metres below the ground surface, thus preventing percolation by meltwater from the snowfields, leading to substantial summer flows of surface water. This meltwater was often of a significant volume, possessing substantial erosive power and carrying large amounts of rock debris.

Following the replacement of Peri-glacial conditions by temperate conditions, these valleys became **Dry Valleys**, due to the loss of groundwater run-off and the absence of any stream. (Apart from certain brief exceptions today such as surface water flows due to severe weather and inappropriate cultivation of arable land). A substantial example is Cradle Valley (grid ref: TQ 494020), observable from the Seaford to Alfriston road. Along the cliff-line, most Dry valleys are termed 'hanging', as their former seaward extensions have been removed by coast-line recession during the last 10,000 years. The early coast line would have been more indented, but locally it now has a straight north-west to south-east orientation. An exposed coastal deposit of Coombe Rock can be viewed at Birling Gap (grid ref: TV 552960), where this mechanically weak material is exposed to wave erosion.

Text Box No. 12. COOMBE DEPOSIT, consists of accumulated frost shattered chalk debris carried downhill by meltwater at the end of the Devensian Glaciation. It can become a number of metres thick and is composed of pieces of Chalk set within a chalk mud. Sometimes this mixture becomes re-calcified, or cemented together into a hard homogenous rock referred to as COOMBE ROCK.

Besides the Dry valleys referred to above, another common feature of the Downland landscape dating from the Devensian Glaciation are the small, scalloped-shaped valleys or hollows that are termed **Coombes**. A typical example may be observed at Exceat and is actually named Coombe Bottom (grid ref: TV 521989). An unusual example is the magnificent Deep Dean (grid ref: TQ 540026), south of Wilmington. These were created by solifluction and meltwater action during the brief cool springs and summers experienced during this glacial period and the spell immediately following it. Work carried out on the identification of various fossilised beetles alive at this time, have established that the mean July temperature would have been in the region of 7-8 degrees Celsius.

Other evidence of the last throes of this period and the cold conditions that immediately followed, can occasionally be seen in the Seven Sisters Country Park in the form of Coombe Deposits (grid ref: TV 520988) and **Involutions** (grid ref: TV 518981). These two sites, both situated at the base of hillsides, exhibit the results of solifluction. At the latter, Coombe Deposit has been frost-heaved into a series of ridges approximately a half-metre high. Involutions are the runnels between the ridges which were gouged deeper by surface water run-off and later filled with **Loess** (Text Box No. 13), a wind blown silt deposited during latter cold dry periods.

Text Box No. 13. LOESS, (from Swiss German lösch), is a fine, reddish, wind-blown type of deposit or, the soil derived from it. It comes from glacial deposits where glacial activity has ground rocks down to a very fine dust. When dry, loess can be highly susceptible to wind erosion, and downwind deposits may become very thick. They are geologically unstable even under natural conditions. Loess grains are angular with little rounding or polishing and are composed of crystals of quartz, feldspar, mica and other minerals. It is highly erodible by water or wind and soils underlain by loess tend to be very free draining. As the grains weather, they release minerals which means that soils containing loess are often very fertile.

CHAPTER 4
Towards Today's Landscape

The pre-glacial river systems of south-eastern England have shown little adjustment to today's coastline, formed by the English Channel between Beachy Head and Sandwich in Kent. The coastline of East Sussex may be traced back to the period following the creation of the Strait of Dover. This commenced at about 18,000 years B.P., with a build up of 'ponded' glacial meltwater in what is now the southern North Sea. This rose and gouged out deep channels across the land bridge connecting the British Isles with the continent. Later, the rising sea level flooded along the river systems that had formed, severing the land bridge at about 8,500 years B.P., eventually eroding away any temporarily formed islands (Figure No. 8). Sea level continued to rise until between 2-3,000 years B.P., and has since fluctuated only a few metres either way of today's level. The 'coastline,' that familiar boundary line placed on maps which becomes a unchanging assumption in peoples minds, is in fact a dynamic, natural functioning entity in itself; because maps place this boundary between the sea and land in a fixed position, at a fixed time, that is not to say that it will not change; it will! That boundary - the coastline in conjunction with the global sea level, is now being significantly influenced by man-induced **Climate Change**.

As the earth's ice caps and snowfields retreated, so a rapid recovery of sea-level took place over the next few thousand years and is recorded in complex sequences of mineral and organic sediment infillings along the valleys of the Cuckmere, Ouse, and Adur. Sea-level stood at approximately 27 metres below O.D. at 9,000 years B.P., 15 metres below O.D. at 7,500 years B.P. and at 5 metres below O.D. at 5,500 years B.P. It was during this period that brackish, and then marine, conditions penetrated into what are now the floodplain sections of the main Sussex river valleys. Between about 5,000 and 3,200 years B.P. inundation created a strongly embayed coast, with well-developed long narrow sea inlets, or **Drowned Valleys** (Text Box No.

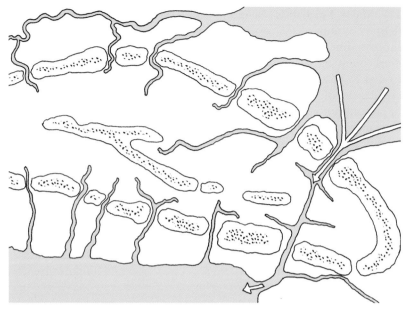

Figure no.8.1 Formation of the Dover Straits.

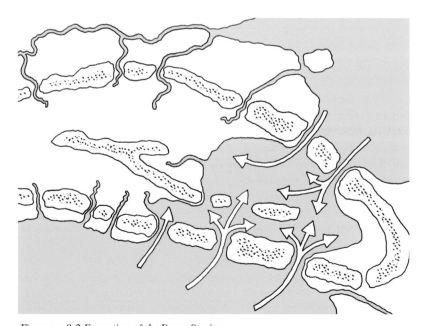

Figure no.8.2 Formation of the Dover Straits.

14). Major headlands, especially Beachy Head, were probably well defined by about 5,000 years B.P., with a consequent reduction of long-shore sediment movement around them. Sedimentation of the formerly open embayments along the Sussex coast was probably also controlled by locally complex relationships between the growth and periodic breaching of shingle barriers and the response of estuary shape, in accommodating longer-term fluctuations to tidal cycles. The Cuckmere was an estuarine inlet by about 5,000 years B.P., penetrating inland to as far as present day Alfriston. There is evidence of marine erosion of the 5 metre high cliffed slope on the eastern side of the valley just south of the Park Centre at Exceat (grid ref: TV 521993). Estuarine sediments below modern **Alluvium** (Text Box No. 15) suggest that mudflat formation may have commenced as early as 4,500 years B.P. Boreholes sunk close to the western margin of the valley, in connection with the reconstruction of Exceat Bridge (grid ref: TV 514992) revealed the following strata: Sand and silt down to a depth of 5.20 metres underlain by a layer of flint down to 6.50 metres; below this lay fairly soft chalk down to the chalk bedrock at 13.40 metres.

Text Box No. 14. DROWNED VALLEYS are almost always estuaries formed when sea levels rise (or land level falls), leading to valleys which were previously at or close to sea level, becoming submerged. The result is often a very large estuary at the mouth of a relatively insignificant river. Following the last cold period, valleys would have initially also have been partially infilled by erosion of the extensive sand-rich Quaternary deposits which overlay much of the area.

A number of sites along the margins of the lower valley exhibit the remains of degraded **Sea Cliffs**, examples being at grid refs: TV 521975, 520990, 511995. Fluvial Incision ceased approximately 9,500 years B.P. This date has been deduced from peat deposits exposed during the construction of Arlington Reservoir during the late 1960's (grid ref: TQ 538074) and have been radiocarbon dated to 9,435 years B.P. ± 120 years. Looking at the Ouse valley, evidence of brackish conditions at the present day river mouth, have been dated to approximately 6,300 years B.P., using radiocarbon dating of organic sediments.

From about 3,000 years B.P., terrestrial sedimentation became dominant over marine induced alluvium sedimentation, which steadily converted estuarine embayments into river **Floodplains** (Text Box No. 16). Evidence also exists of the presence of seams of peat being deposited during this process. Human-induced acceleration of this process came from clearance of the extensive forest, which by then clothed most of the landscape and land cultivation which had commenced in the **Neolithic Age**. Large-scale **Soil Erosion** took place, reaching a peak during the **Bronze** and **Iron Ages** and was a significant cause of this relatively abrupt change in environmental conditions. This has brought about the thin, nutrient poor soils that exist across so much of the Downs today. Research carried out on the North Downs has disclosed that on some of the lower downland slopes, a buried top soil exists beneath large amounts of chalky subsoil, or hillwash. Similar conditions are almost certainly to have occurred on the South Downs. These events would have resembled the soil erosion problems being experienced in some Third World countries today.

Text Box No. 15. ALLUVIUM is the unconsolidated, loose material deposited by a river or stream. A river system is continually picking up and dropping small particles of silt, sand and rock from along its entire length. Since the capacity of a watercourse to carry matter in suspension is reliant upon its velocity, any circumstances tending to retard the rate of flow, will reduce suspension. Thus a fall in the gradient of the river or stream channel, or any obstruction or situation leading the watercourse to overflow, will dissipate energy allowing more particles to be dropped than carried. Once consolidated, these areas of alluvium are referred to as Alluvial or Floodplains.

It is probable that the East Sussex coastline was still well embayed or indented in Romano-British times, and that the lowermost sections of the Cuckmere, Ouse and Adur valleys persisted as natural tidal basins as late as the twelfth century A.D. Thus, the broad arcing form of today's coastline between Shoreham-by-Sea and Beachy Head is largely a feature of the modern historical period.

Text Box No. 16. FLOODPLAINS often border a river or stream and form areas of relatively level land that are inundated from time to time during high river levels. Floodplains are often composed of alluvium, silts, loam and organic matter and can support rich assemblages of wildlife and are often referred to as 'riparian zones;' they also frequently form valuable pasture for agriculture. Older floodplain deposits are often present as benches or terraces, above the current day floodplain; these are referred to as Terrace Deposits e.g. west of Lullington Court (grid ref: TQ 523025) and south of Berwick Court Farm (grid ref: TQ 525041). Development has often unwisely taken place on them, as they are level and easy to develop; however they can be disastrously prone to flooding.

CHAPTER 5
Cuckmere River

During the last 5,000 years, the original estuarine inlet of the river Cuckmere, has been progressively infilled by sedimentation, a process that was also accelerated by the eastwards growth of a shingle barrier or beach, fed by both longshore drift and from onshore movement of shingle. This caused the mouth of the river to be deflected eastwards, with periodic closure due to intermittent, increased onshore or longshore supplies of sediment. Later, tidal flow was further reduced due to the process of **Inning** within the lower Floodplain. Inning is the term given to the building of floodbanks to partially enclose a given area of **Saltmarsh** (a vegetated area regularly flooded during high tides) or Floodplain to regularise tidal flooding in order to assist further deposition of silt or alluvium to form grazing pasture.

Changes of the position of the Cuckmere's mouth due to Longshore Drift (Text Box No. 17), are known from throughout the period dating back to the late 18th century, it having entered the sea at various points between the chalk cliffs on either side of the valley. The river mouth is now restrained in its approximate late 18th century position by training walls (groyne-like structures) originally introduced in the 1940's, but subsequently upgraded during the 1970's. This has induced the formation of a small shingle delta with a shifting pattern of minor channels. Severe short-term blockage of the river entrance by shingle was recorded in July 1912, which caused extensive floodplain inundation.

The famous **Meanders** of the River Cuckmere have been brought about by two main forces: firstly, the seaward slope of the 'recent' alluvial floor of the valley is so gradual that the river rather than taking the shortest most direct course to the sea, meanders rather like spilt water on a flat surface. Secondly, rivers tend to flow with a spiral action like a helix, spiralling downstream. Where the current flows against the edge of the river channel it tends to remove material from one side depositing it on the opposite side and so a meander slowly forms.

River meanders along the natural course of the River Cuckmere at Exceat.

The earliest detailed document relating to the Cuckmere is from the Water Court of the Cuckmere, dated July 27 1618; an extract follows, together with explanations to assist the reader: "It ys ordered and decreed that the common sewer [river] betweene Brokehole [Brock Hole Bottom] and Cessingham bridge [Sessingham near Arlington] shallbe made 20 foote wyde in all places wher now it is narrower and that for the doing thereof a scott [charge] of 3s. [15 pence] the acre ys granted of all the lands lying betweene Excete bridge and Cessingham bridge and of all the freshe [fresh water] marshe betweene the said bridge and the sea."

This document gives us a close insight of the river in the early 17th century together with some of the issues which landowners and farmers then faced. Of interest, is that the Court ordered that the width of the river the river should be increased to a width of 6.1 metres (20 feet) where it was narrower, between Brock Hole Bottom and Sessingham Bridge. This shows that much of this section of the river has been widened by man over the years, for southward of Longbridge, which is north of Alfriston, no section of the river now narrows to near this width. This meeting of the Water Court also brought about the surveying and drawing of the first detailed map of the Cuckmere valley, carried out that same year, 1618. The map shows that the layout of meadows and their intersecting ditches has scarcely changed through 500 years.

There is also mention made of a 'freshwater marsh' between Exceat Bridge and the sea. Inning appears to have taken place in four distinct phases south of Exceat Bridge (Figure No. 9). These are as follows: the first phase on the west side of the river, involved the northern half of Chyngton Brooks (grid ref: TV 514986); this would have been protected by a floodbank which still forms part of the present west river bank. Along the southern side protection was afforded by Shepherds Bank, a large bank and ditch running east-west across the meadows; these type of constructions are sometimes referred to as borrow banks as a ditch was excavated to create material for the bank. The second phase of inning would have extended seawards of the above on to what is nowadays the low foreshore. Both phases are of medieval origin, as is the third phase of inning behind the east bank and lying between the southern end of the Meanders and the sea (grid ref: TV 517979). The fourth area of inning we shall look at a little further on.

Winter flooding within Cuckmere valley south of Litlington.

During times of heavy rainfall or fast thaws, flooding has been a regular, natural occurrence within the Cuckmere valley and parts of the river's catchment area directly north of the Downs, where the heavy impermeable clays rely greatly on the Cuckmere for drainage. Drainage was not helped by the tortuous natural course taken by the river, the Meanders considerably reducing its discharge seaward, especially when the additional effects of tide are added to the equation.

During the agricultural revolution of the 18th and 19th centuries, the then Commissioners for the levels decided to improve the drainage situation by **River Realignment** (Figure No. 9).

The first improvement was carried out just to the north of Ewe Down where two short, loops existed in the river's course (grid ref: TQ 512001); here, a channel or 'cut' some 450 metres (500 yards) in length was constructed. As to the date of this work, the 1813 ordnance survey map shows the cut in existence where as Gardener and Gream's map of 1795 shows the river still flowing through the two loops. After this work had been carried out, the former loops became bays which only flooded during spring tides, supporting areas of Saltmarsh vegetation. During re-construction of the river bank in 1958, these bays were finally isolated from the course of the river, levelled and now form pasture.

The final piece of river channel alignment was a more ambitious piece of engineering by far, involving the by-passing of the extensive Meanders south of Exceat Bridge. This also created the fourth phase land to be Inned. The natural course of the Cuckmere involved it travelling a distance of 1.7 miles (2.75kms.) from Exceat Bridge and the adjacent medieval causeway, to the sea; with realignment, the more direct course resulted in this distance being reduced to just over one mile. It was also hoped that the improved flow of the river would reduce the build up of shingle within the river mouth. The decision to embark on this work was taken at a General Session of the Commissioners of Sewers for the Levels of Cuckmere on May 21 1846. The plan agreed upon, called for the construction of a new eastern riverbank alongside the new river channel, so preventing the entry of the tide into the existing meandering river channel and adjacent floodplain. This major piece of work was completed within a year, involving the excavation of 18,969 cubic metres of spoil, which together with the installation of sluices, cost £751.85! (Figure No. 9).

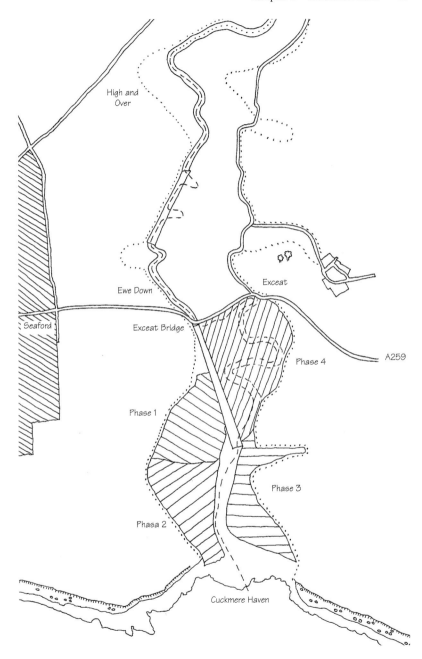

Figure no.9 Cuckmere River Realignments.

CHAPTER 6
Chalk Cliffs

The various strata of the Chalk with their varying composition and fossil content create varying qualities in respect to their fracture patterns, porosity and rock strength. It is these qualities (together with climate and sea level) that control the erosion rates along the Chalk cliffs.

Additionally during the Ice Age, cold climate weathering reduced the coherence and stability of sub-surface Chalk and added other structural properties that also contribute to cliff failure along this coastline. Most cliff-falls are small scale, involving the detachment of wedge-shaped pieces of rock. Cliff top fissures, parallel to the cliff face, occur periodically. They promote block detachment via the rock shearing, occasionally creating substantial falls in excess of 50-70,000 tonnes (e.g. Seven Sisters, 1925; Seaford Head, 1986; Beachy Head, 1813 and 1999).

Currently, there are several weathering processes involved in reducing the stability of Chalk cliffs. Wetting and drying cycles tend to have most effect on the thin seams and bands of clay and silty-clay within the Chalk. Heavy rainfall can also occur in summer, when there may have been shrinkage of clays following drought conditions; under these conditions, groundwater can trigger large falls.

However, a majority of cliff-falls are due to weathering and erosion occurring during the harsher weather experienced during the winter. At Cow Gap east of Beachy Head, the clays that underlie the Chalk cause movement by slippage aided by groundwater seepage, so causing the chalks to slump in great landslips. Maximum wave energy is experienced along the shoreline between Seaford Head and Beachy Head and is higher in comparison to much of the remaining coastline of south-east and central southern England. This is the result of its orientation in relation to both the prevalent and largest waves. In this respect, the influence of rock structure and resistance is probably subsidiary to wave forces in determining rates of cliff base and shore

Landslips between Cow Gap and Beachy Head.

erosion. Notching at the foot of the cliffs is active, creating comparatively short-lived caves. One example, 'Parson Darby's Hole,' was artificially modified in the 18th century to provide sanctuary for shipwrecked crews; it had totally disappeared by 1930. All of these processes can open up fissures to critical widths and depths

Clay replacing chalk remover by solution along joints and cracks.

Where groundwater had over long periods in the past, percolated through the Chalk perhaps having passed through slightly acidic overlying deposits, Chalk was removed by the process of solution, gradually widening fractures and joints, creating solution pipes (or swallow holes). This took place mainly within warmer and wetter climatic phases; these were then filled during a later period with Clay with Flint and Tertiary deposits, such as may be observed at Seaford Head. Some of these exposures give exceptional examples of the geological story through great tracts of time, for example: at Hope Gap (grid ref: TV 510973) and the adjoining Short Cliff (grid ref: TV 512974), various overlying Tertiary and Quaternary period deposits in the form of pebbly marine deposits, sands, clays, chalk debris and loess. These deposits are prone to cliff falls after spells of heavy rainfall, which can occur in both summer and winter. Beneath Beachy Head, there is a cave system which is known to extend into the Chalk for some 400 metres.

CHAPTER 7
Coast And Shingle

Along the coastline of south-east England, beaches are almost entirely composed of fragments of flint which have been rounded by sea-induced abrasion and often discoloured to a light brown by exposure to iron compounds within the sea water. Along this coast, shingle is being continuously swept eastwards by a process termed **Longshore Drift** (Text Box No. 17), the material terminating in the vast shingle peninsula of Dungeness. Rates of longshore movement are almost everywhere falling, primarily due to a decreasing supply of shingle from off-shore sources and cliff-falls. Consequently, many beaches now have a history of shingle loss, producing steep beach gradients.

Much of this offshore supply could have been derived from former raised beaches and Coombe Rock deposits, the latter being rich in weathered flint. The Cuckmere, Ouse, Adur and Arun, would have contributed additional coarse sediment through Fluvial Incision and when draining the tundra-like environment associated with Peri-glacial conditions. All this material would have been reworked and redistributed during the complex sequence of climate and sea-level changes. Substantial input would also derive from the earlier erosion of Chalk bedrock, a process which would have bevelled some miles from off the Chalk outcrop. This implies a once abundant supply of flint to build shingle barrier structures along the entire length of the shoreline of East Sussex. It is considered that the major period of barrier growth was 3,000 to 2,300 years B.P., a period of exceptional storminess, as confirmed from sites elsewhere such as Dungeness. To the east, Willingdon Levels and the Crumbles provide further evidence of a complex sequence of events involving cyclic erosion and deposition linked to shingle barrier growth and breakdown. Willingdon Levels during the period 5,000 - 3,000 years B.P., was a tidal embayment that interrupted longshore drift. Once sea-level stabilised, the barrier extended completely across the seaward entrance.

Text Box No. 17. LONGSHORE DRIFT is the process by which material is moved along a shoreline. The process arises when waves approach the shore at an oblique angle, this is often determined by the prevailing wind. This causes the wave swash together with sand and shingle to move up the beach at an angle. The backwash however, carries the material back down the beach at a right angle. The process can cause significant erosion which, in relation to developed areas, is of serious concern. (Figure No. 10). The process was also responsible for frequently changing the position of river estuaries as already mentioned in Chapter 5; during the medieval period, the Ouse entered the sea at Splash Point, Seaford then being a port.

During the 19th and much of the 20th century the problem of erosion had been addressed through the use of control structures, particularly sets of **Groynes**. Where cliff base sea defences have been put in place together with cliff re-profiling measures, e.g. Peacehaven to Brighton, current coastal erosion rates have been dramatically reduced. Most of these works date to the early years of the 20th century, with major works undertaken in the early 1930's and also during the 1970's. Research has concluded that 36% of the former yield of shingle from cliff erosion between Rottingdean and Beachy Head has been lost due to shoreline defence and protection. Since the mid 1980's, emphasis has moved to shingle replenishment and recycling as

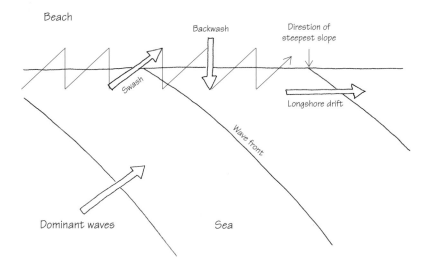

Figure no. 10 Longshore Drift

a means of long-term beach management, exemplified by sites such as Seaford, Eastbourne and Pevensey Bay.

The small beaches between Seaford and Birling Gap have been retreating, although the broad shingle barrier spit that has grown across the mouth of the former Cuckmere tidal inlet has grown over recent years. This barrier has a more complex history than appears on first sight, having arisen as a result of both natural and man-induced processes.

Shingle extraction taking place during 1958, using dragline and narrow guage railway.

During 1932, proposals were considered by the Cuckmere Catchment Board, the body then charged with responsibility for land drainage within the valley. The Board wished to construct a light railway between the river mouth, and an area opposite the farm buildings at Exceat where a wharf was to be built. The purpose for the bringing about of this scheme was for **Shingle Extraction** from the river estuary to reduce the build up of shingle that was impeding the river's flow, thereby improving the drainage efficiency of the river system. The plan proposed that once the shingle had been transported to Exceat, it would then be sold for use as aggregate to the building trade. Another aspect of the shingle beaches at Cuckmere was that during the 1920's and 1930's, flint boulders referred to as 'blue boulders,' were collected by gangs of men from off the foreshore, for use in the building trade, or in industrial processes. Trade in this commodity was also carried on at both Newhaven and Langney near Eastbourne; at Langney trade continued until the 1970's. Due to a lack of river maintenance during the years of the Second World War, large shoals of shingle built up within the river mouth and extending for a short distance upstream. These were dealt with by the use of explosives which hurled large plumes of water and shingle high into the air!

Driving shot holes for explosives and river bed being blasted, 1951.

The Chalk extends seawards by way of a **Wave-cut Platform**, varying in width at mean low tide of between 100 and 200 metres; this may be observed and accessed during low tide. These platforms consist of the highly-gullied ('runnels') surface of the remaining Chalk bedrock, after the cliff face has retreated landward. Platform elevation in relation to the mean sea-level is regulated either by position within the tidal range or by differences in the relative hardness of the Chalk strata. Overall, gradient is mostly below 5 degrees, though steps or 'risers' of up to 0.5 metre in height are discernable between different Chalk strata in places. The gradient is usually steepest adjacent to the cliffs, declining seawards.

Seaward of the upper shore, the exposed Chalk bedrock of the platforms are characteristically dissected by gullies running seawards, some 0.5 to 4.0 metres apart and 0.25 to 0.5 metres in width. The intensity of dissection increases seawards, as a result of progressively longer submersion during tidal cycles. At their seaward end, some gullies can be in excess of 1.5 metre deep and 1.0 metre in width and extending below maximum low water, becoming submergent reef-like forms. Ridges between gullies have frequently developed involving

Aerial view of part of Seven Sisters cliffs showing wave-cut platform, gullies, caves and evidence of Iron Age cultivation beneath modern ploughing; 1970's

bands of flints. The lower parts of most platforms are generally, partially or wholly covered by seaweed.

Abrasion during the winter months probably plays a significant part in the erosion of these platform areas. Towards the land, the upper platform levels show greatest evidence of abrasion, an area where limpets *(Patella vulgata)*, do not occur. The freeze-thaw cycles experienced during exceptionally cold weather, cause extensive cracking and spalling (chipping) of exposed Chalk. Prolonged periods of this weather may account for the release of significant amounts of flint. The high limpet population could also be an important contributory process as could the burrowing action by the piddock *(Pholas dactylus)*. Limpets remove Chalk as they graze algae and where they create 'homescars' to which they return for shelter. Rates of erosion across these platforms are considered to be in the order of 1.3-5.0 mm per year of which up to 35% can on some sections, be attributable to a high mollusc population. Therefore in practice, the term 'wave-cut' does need some qualification.

Offshore, out to about 1,000 metres seawards of mean low water, sediments are of predominantly fine to medium sands, silts and silty clays. Local diversity is provided by outcrops of exposed Chalk and areas of well-packed rounded flint cobbles. Beyond approximately 1,000 metres from the coastline, sediments become coarser, with sandy gravels dominating. Most of inner Seaford Bay is occupied by a relatively thick layer of muddy and silty sand.

A problem which successive generations have wrestled with was the accumulation of shingle within the river mouths or estuaries, caused by the continual eastward movement of shingle by Longshore Drift. For example at Cuckmere, as far back as 1582 when a presentment made by "Waterbayley" John Browyn and others stating that "the haven mought ther dyrun tymes in wynter ys stopped with preble stones by reson wherof the hole levell ys drowned and that we cannot be suffered to cut the same haven up." Until the construction of a groyne to retain the shingle to the west of the river mouth (possibly during the 1940's?), the river would periodically change the point at which it issued into the sea. The actual known extremes of this cycle were 1874 when the river mouth lay half way along the present east beach, and 1908 when it lay half way between the present position and the coastguard cottages to the west of the Haven. The river mouth was finally stabilised during the early 1970's with the construction of a second retaining groyne along its eastern side.

PART 2 - TODAY'S LANDSCAPE

CHAPTER 8
River Realignment

Today, the lower reaches of the Cuckmere valley with its relict Meanders and its arcing shingle beach, forms a much managed landscape, with the 1846 river channel or 'cut' surrounded by pasture claimed from the sea. The natural course of the river - the iconic Meanders, now lies fossilised and isolated from the tidal section of the river. These Meanders are broadening in width from wind induced wave action causing consequential silting up and accumulation of natural debris. This lack of flow and build-up of silt has created an environment of low biodiversity, which additionally during hot weather suffers from low oxygen levels leading to high fish mortality.

The estuary is currently maintained at considerable expense by a number of wooden retaining walls and groynes assisted by an annual shingle dredging programme. The river banks between the estuary and north to Exceat Bridge are now reaching the end of their serviceable life. These structures are increasingly ineffective against a rising sea level.

In Spring 2001 a new partnership, the *'Cuckmere Estuary Restoration Partnership'* was formed between the Environment Agency, English Nature, the National Trust and the Sussex Downs Conservation Board, to consider restoration to a naturally functioning river estuary and floodplain. This would accommodate Climate Change and allow a more biodiverse estuarine habitat to develop, providing a natural progression from grazing marsh to Saltmarsh to mudflats. This would also help meet international obligations to both halt the loss and to restore such habitats wherever possible. With the floodplain restored, the existing Meanders would then once again function as part of the intertidal habitat.

The scheme was originally planned with a two-phase approach, initially dealing with controlled flooding of the National Trust-owned Chyngton Brooks area by the breaching of selected short sections of river bank. This was to be followed at a later date by a similar scheme

Dredging of shingle from mouth of River Cuckmere in 1991; also shown are the modern training walls.

on the eastern side of the valley. Detailed findings from the Environment Agency's modeling of the relative sea and land levels showed that if the two-phased approach were to be adopted, the increased flow and velocity of water would lead to the collapse of the river mouth and east bank defences well ahead of the planned schedule.

In February 2004 it was decided to carry out further research into a simultaneous breach approach, which led to a delay in the proposed planning application. This review, as well as considering flood defence issues, will seek to ensure that economic, ecological and recreational interests are fully understood and carefully considered. Following completion of this review the Partnership will develop a revised proposal for the future management of the estuary.

A significant number of local residents and businesses opposed the plans of the Environment Agency, leading to the creation of the pressure group *'Rescue The Cuckmere Valley.'* They claim, with only limited justification, taking into account the broader picture that the risks are: (the authors views are in parentheses):

- Collapse of the sea wall which protects the Coastguard Cottages, endangering their future. [With sea level rise the cottages will have only a limited lifespan].

- Many years of vast areas of mud until salt marsh develops and this only occurring at the fringes. [This could be partly true].

- The flood risk could be increased for villages such as Alfriston and Litlington; the A259 coast road would also be at greater risk of flooding and could be undermined by the Meanders.

- Removal of habitat for the many creatures including badgers that inhabit the valley. [In the medium term, this loss could be made up by a significantly richer bird fauna].

- Loss of the beach on the east of the river once the river is reverted to its original course next to the Seven Sisters. [An extensive beach is likely to remain].

- The loss of popular riverside footpaths. [An alternative route has been planned along the base of the neighbouring hillside].

- Because mud is less attractive than the grass downland scenery this would be damaging to local businesses. [The scheme will not affect downland pasture, but, the saltmarsh is likely to draw in significant 'eco-tourists'].

During 2004 the situation was further compounded by a proposal from several local residents, leading to an outline planning application for the existing river banks to be raised, involving substantial movement of materials. The outcomes of both of these proposals are still pending and are likely to lead to the holding of a planning enquiry. Climate Change and rising sea levels however, will necessitate change in the way low-lying coastal areas are managed in the future. The lack of any urban development in the Cuckmere valley and the changed requirements for agriculture also mean there is little economic justification for spending public money on rebuilding the current flood defences.

CHAPTER 9
The Chalk Cliff-Scape

S mall volume cliff falls are frequent, occurring more often during the months of winter and spring. Large-scale cliff failure events however, only occur on average once every 50 to 60 years. These large-scale events can yield between 50-100,000 cubic metres of Chalk. Fanning out across the Wave-cut Platform, cliff fall debris has a short life as it is rapidly broken down and quickly redistributed by the sea, creating sediment plumes of milky-coloured sea during high tide. Eventually all that is left behind are arc-shaped ridges of chalk boulders marking the former limit of the debris. At the base of the cliffs, caves often develop along joints and primary fractures and may contribute to cliff falls.

Beachy Head is a geologically complex headland, with its southeast facing slopes, truncating the Escarpment of the South Downs. Between Cow Gap and Beachy Head lighthouse, there are pronounced fault failures that generate land slippage (assisted by water and the under lying clay), rock slippage at oblique angles and falls. The major fall that occurred at Beachy Head during January 1999 was most probably triggered by a prolonged spell of wet weather. This event released some 75-80,000 tonnes, burying the cliff base to a height of up to 10 metres. A cliff top retreat rate for this section has been calculated of 0.3 to 0.5 metres per year during the period 1875 – 1979. Conversely, some parts of this section including the highest cliffs west towards Belle Tout are remarkably stable, receding at a rate of less than 0.1 metres per year. There are no sea defence structures along this section except for Groynes at Holywell towards Eastbourne.

The cliff line from Belle Tout to Cuckmere Haven including the famous Seven Sisters, has developed at right angles to the Dip Slope of the Chalk and truncates some eight Dry Valleys that rise landward. Erosion is high due to the complexity of the angle of primary rock joints and a low elevation Wave-cut Platform, that in turn, allows full exposure to the south-westerly approaching waves. Joint controlled

Short Cliff with Tertiary Deposits; Wave-cut Platform at low tide; former sea cliff running inland

falls of Chalk here can create detached rock masses of up to 10,000 cubic metres. Maps and photographic evidence from the past 100 years indicate that the Seven Sisters cliffs have maintained a near vertical face over this period. Overall, with an averaged, uniform erosion rate of 0.51 metres per year for the period 1873-1962, the consensus is that this section is eroding at rates equal to, or above the regional average.

In contrast, the cliffs at and immediately adjacent to Birling Gap, have been subject to detailed attention not least because of the threat posed by their retreat to the survival of cliff-top properties. At a public enquiry held during the 1990's, several independent experts observed that recession rates here were faster than to the east or west. This is partially the result of the Coombe Rock in-filling of the dry valley, with intensely shattered Chalk bedrock beneath descending to below the level of the shingle beach. Coombe Rock with its low mechanical strength fails readily when saturated. Erosion may also be assisted by the even lower elevation of the Wave-cut Platform at Birling Gap. Accentuating the problem, Chalk to the east of Birling Gap lacks marl seams and has a lower density of major joints.

Wealden District Council and its predecessor have conducted annual monitoring of cliff top retreat between Birling Gap and Cuckmere Haven since 1951. Calculations, which integrated cliff retreat during the period 1874-1975, reveal a range between 0.64 and 1.41 metres per year. Rates for recent decades (post 1960) are higher than the longer-term averages.

Between Cuckmere Haven and Seaford Head, Tertiary deposits over lie much of the Chalk, reaching a depth of some 9 metres and often staining the cliff face. In places, it has in-filled vertical solution-widened fissures and Solution Pipes, these occasionally descending to the cliff base. Cliff falls in places are caused by inclined fractures resulting in slippage at an oblique angle, as does slippage of the over-lying Tertiary Deposit where it is at its thickest such as at Short Cliff and Seaford Head. At Hope Gap, an in-filled truncated Dry Valley, solid Chalk has been replaced by various deposits as already referred to, this locally increasing the rate of cliff erosion. A local feature of the Wave-cut Platform occurs near Hope Gap, where, there are a number of circular depressions with raised rims. In addition slightly sinuous gutters have developed broadly along the principal joints. These have been interpreted as truncated solution pipes; developing examples are visible in the face of the cliffs at Short Cliff and Seaford Head. Calculations, of the maximum rates of erosion for this section arrive at a figure of 1.26 metres per year for the period 1925-1955, although it is considered that cliff top recession at Seaford Head was only 0.3 metres per

Massive chalk buttress and seams of flint below Seven Sisters cliffs.

Remains of solution pipe on wave-cut platform below Short Cliff.

Solution pipe below Short Cliff.

year during the period 1875-1980. Due to cliff erosion, less than half of the Iron Age hillfort situated on the summit of Seaford Head now survives. Calculations in relation to the cliff line position at the time of its construction, infer a retreat rate of 0.25 and 0.35 metres per year over the past 2,500 years. Sea defence structures are limited to concrete blocks at Splash Point and a short sea wall below the south-east facing cliffs and cottages at Cuckmere Haven. Apart from these, cliff erosion and retreat is a continuing natural process producing near vertical cliffs up to 85 metres in height.

Looking to the future, Climate Change may well in

the medium-term, lead to increased rainfall and also enhanced wave erosion, leading to an intensification of the existing process. In conclusion, cliff failure is intermittent, controlled by the rate of opening up and downward penetration of fissures.

CHAPTER 10
Shingle Beaches

Currently along the coastline between Brighton and Eastbourne, there is an annual deposition of shingle reaching perhaps 25,000 tonnes, due to chalk cliff erosion occurring at an average rate of half metre per year. The amounts being fed into this system from the earlier mentioned offshore deposits are now much decreased due to natural exhaustion and sea defences.

Between Birling Gap and Cuckmere Haven, a section that receives high wave energy, beaches are now characterised by being discontinuous and narrow, having retreated and steepened since the late 19th century. The major shingle deposit along this section is the pocket of beach occupying the Birling Gap embayment. The length of this beach however, has reduced by some 800 metres since 1874. It is calculated that some 1615 cubic metres of fresh flints per year are derived from erosion of the cliffs and Wave-cut Platform along the Seven Sisters cliffs section. Observations show that losses of shingle are greatest when waves approach from the south-east. The entire beach has been removed at Birling Gap for brief periods at least three times during winter storms since 1930, the most recent occasion being in 1996.

During the 1950s, the weak sea defences at Cuckmere Haven due to a lack of shingle east of the river mouth, were causing concern to the then East Sussex River Board. During the winter of 1959-60, a groyne was constructed at Cliff End to reduce the amount of shingle being carried eastward from Cuckmere Haven by the Longshore Drift. The following winter, with the cessation of shingle extraction from Cuckmere Haven (referred to in Chapter 7), the Board purchased the privately owned light railway complete with its locomotive and trucks. The track was then lifted and re-laid to run eastwards from the river mouth along what little remained of the shingle ridge. A large amount of shingle was then dredged from the river mouth area by dragline, transported by the railway and tipped; this was then pushed up into a substantial ridge by bulldozer. This explains the steep backslope to the

Groyne being constructed at Cliff End, to reduce longshor drift; 1960.

present day beach profile, which together with natural accretion, has led to the significant shingle beach or barrier now existing at Cuckmere Haven. This process has been augmented by the small leakage of shingle from the Shingle Replenishment works completed at Seaford in 1987. To the west of the river, man has also substantially

Dragline loading narrow guage railway trucks near estuary; 1960.

Shingle being emptied from trucks midway along shingle ridge; 1960.

modified the shingle by annually re-building the shingle ridge with shingle dredged from out of the estuary.

At Seaford Beach, erosion and depletion were the dominant features, with shingle being difficult to retain, as it tended to move rapidly alongshore or, offshore. The position of the mean low water line

Winter beach scene 1990's, showing storm ridges.

moved 107 metres landwards, between 1879 and 1961. The first groynes were constructed at Tide Mills (towards Newhaven) in 1836, followed by construction of a seawall between the Buckle area (grid ref: TV 469997) and Tide Mills in the 1880's.

It is thought that shingle by-passed Newhaven Harbour up to the construction of its breakwater in 1844. After construction of the breakwater and pier, by-passing appears to have been reduced, creating a substantial beach to the west of Newhaven. Significant erosion of the central section of Seaford beach occurred within a few years, leading to the erection of some 80 closely-spaced wooden groynes and the upgrading and extension of the seawall. The new breakwater also introduced a reversal of longshore drift to the west of Tide Mills because of localised change in wave behaviour.

Although there was some periodic deposition at either end of the beach between the Buckle area and Tidemills and between Splash Point and Seaford Head, progressive lowering and steepening of the beach was experienced up to the late 1970's. This was despite recharging with shingle taken from Dungeness in 1936 and 1958 and the construction of a number of long groynes in the late 1950's. Further attempts at shingle recycling carried out in the early 1960's, utilised accumulated shingle from against the east pier of Newhaven Harbour.

The then considered view then was that the prime cause was the effect of the western breakwater of Newhaven Harbour, substantially intercepting potential longshore drift. This line of reasoning ignored the fact that there had been several occasions of the beach being drawn and lowered seawards and the breaching of the beach, (the most recent in 1875 causing severe flooding to the town). It was becoming apparent that the seawall and groynes actually promoted both drawdown and scour whilst erosion of the Chalk platform which forms the beach foundation was seen as another cause, this having lowered by some 3 metres between 1900 and 1950. Experimental studies carried out by the Hydraulics Research Station in 1961-62, demonstrated that shingle had a tendency to move offshore when wave heights exceeded 4 metres. The shingle did not return if deposited into deep water or if it was incorporated into the silt-clay and fine sand layer covering much of the seabed.

The Southern Water Authority took on management responsibility for Seaford beach from the Newhaven and Seaford Sea Defence Commissioners in 1981, and commissioned the Hydraulics Research Station to carry out a range of studies to determine appropriate measures to secure the future integrity of the beach. This work concluded with a recommendation to replenish the beach with 1,450,000 cubic metres of shingle taken from off-shore deposits off West Sussex. **Shingle Replenishment** took place along a total frontage of some 2,500 metres, together with modifying the town's former sewer outfall at Splash Point (grid ref: TV 488981) to form a large terminal groyne to contain eastward longshore drift. This work, the largest operation of its kind at the time, was carried out during 1987 with beach specifications such as a crest height of 6.5 metres above O.D. and a crest width of 25 metres. The work was largely completed just in time to protect Seaford from the 1987 storm.

With the intermediate groynes now buried beneath the raised shingle, this created a deposition of some extra 50,000-70,000 cubic metres per year just west of the terminal groyne, therefore necessitating routine recycling within the beach system. Losses of some 15% by volume were anticipated within 6 months of the schemes completion, mostly due to removal of finer material. Monitoring carried out shortly after completion of the beach replenishment, revealed a close correlation with the theory. Monitoring has since revealed a pattern of losses and gains over different sections of the beach, with gains recorded at both eastern and western ends; these are equalised through periodic recycling by machinery. Average annual gains are of some 13,800 cubic metres; the maximum deposition was in 1992 with 65,000 cubic metres and the maximum depletion in 2000 of 75,000 cubic metres. Recycling has thus sustained the equilibrium of this modified beach.

PART 3 – TODAY'S LANDSCAPE 2

CHAPTER 11
Topography

T he Cuckmere Valley is situated towards the eastern extremity of the South Downs, where the relatively soft Chalk rock is truncated by the relentless advance of the sea. The valley has been created by the smallest of the five main rivers of Sussex, namely the River Cuckmere, more popularly known as the 'Cuckmere River.' These three features, chalk upland, coastline and river valley, give rise to some of the most unique and spectacular landforms in the British Isles. Stretching westward from Eastbourne, this includes a near complete sequence of the Chalk strata found in southern England.

Agriculture commenced at about 7,000 B.P., when the first Neolithic people started to arrive on the coasts of south-east England, they being the first people actually to carry out farming, that is, to keep domesticated livestock and cultivate crops. Undoubtedly, they still supplemented their food with hunter-gatherer techniques. Although the Downs were covered in woodland at that time, man would have been attracted by the often light and easily worked soils to be found upon them. These early agriculturists would have begun with **Woodland Clearance** using flint axes, aided by the agent of fire; the clearings created would then have been cultivated until the soil became exhausted. In the mean time, they would have proceeded to clear further areas, the former clearings then perhaps being used for grazing.

The next important period is centred on the **Iron Age** (700 B.C. to A.D. 43), but overlaps well into the Roman period, for life and technology evolved steadily, and flowed from one archaeological age into the next. During this period, relatively large areas of the Downs were intensively cultivated after clearance of the tree cover, often leading to severe soil erosion problems with soil being washed downhill, and into watercourses. There are two areas where prehistoric (or Celtic) **Field Systems** from this period are discernible; one sprawls across Ewe Down at Chyngton (grid ref: TV 509998) towards the Hindover area. The other area, shown by the remains of low **Lynchets** (banks formed by soil movement due to cultivation), stretches across the hinterland of the western half of the Seven Sisters. In the vicinity of Short Brow (grid ref: TV 530976), additional evidence in the form of pottery sherds suggests a late Iron Age settlement here.

The soils on the Chalk are generally well drained, resulting in poor water retention and are easily workable, although they can differ significantly where Clay with Flint deposits exist. Here, Chalk itself was often applied as 'manure' on these clayey deposits. This helped to ameliorate the heavy and slightly acidic character of these clay soils for wheat production. Evidence of quarrying can be seen by the presence of abandoned chalk pits e.g.Haven Brow (grid ref: TV 525976), Wilmington (grid refs: TQ 541035 & TQ 537035), Berwick (grid ref: TQ 505044) and at BoPeep, Alciston (grid ref: TQ 495051). (Some pits are bomb craters from the Second World War, but reference to the Tithe Map of 1840 can solve individual origins). Soils developed on the steep slopes, often of Rendzina in origin, can be extremely shallow and tending to have a low mineral content. Across these slopes, tiers of parallel paths are often formed due to down hill soil slippage through the centuries, aided by the frequent passage of farm livestock; these are termed **Terracettes**.

By contrast, areas of the Gault and Weald Clays tend to be used

Terracettes along escarpment of the Downs near Alciston.

more for grass production; but locally where lighter, more workable superficial deposits occur, arable cropping is often important. The clay soils however, are subject to water logging for long periods during the winter. The soils in the High Weald are generally clayey, slowly permeable and are seasonally waterlogged. Springs are common at the junction between permeable and impermeable rocks and the steep slopes of valleys are commonly unsuitable for agriculture hence the large amount of scattered woodland cover, (amounting to some 25% of land cover). The High Weald has an abundance of small streams, creating deeply cut and often heavily wooded valleys, known as **Ghylls**. These streams and their attendant semi-natural woodland are often largely unaffected by the actions of man, supporting a rich wildlife. Owing to the relatively impermeable nature of the underlying geology and despite the density of woodland in the High Weald, surface water run-off is high because of the steeper nature of the topography. Stream flows are highly seasonal and respond quickly to heavy rainfall. These streams were once of great importance in helping to power the Sussex iron industry between the second century BC and the 19th century.

By contrast the more open countryside of the Low Weald has generally fewer and larger streams, which are often more heavily modified for drainage. Areas of damp meadows, wet woodland and marsh were previously once common. Owing to the lesser gradients across the Low Weald, watercourses are generally more sluggish than in their upper reaches situated in the High Weald.

Pevensey Levels to the east, and to a lesser extent The Brooks south of Lewes, are drained by heavily modified river channels and interconnecting drainage channels. **Drainage** is managed by pumps and sluices operated to maintain a low water table. Where sympathetically managed, these drains can support a wide range of species. A number of streams rise from the localised greensand at the base of the Chalk and although small in size, maintain a level of flow throughout the year. Although the catchments of these streams are small they flow directly into main rivers including the Cuckmere or through the built-up areas of Polegate and Eastbourne where they can form a potentially significant flood risk.

Many villages (e.g. Wilmington, Berwick, Alciston, Firle), became established along the foot of the Escarpment due to the presence of springs flowing from out of the Chalk. Currently, 70% of the Water Supply in south-east England is sourced from deep within the Chalk by way of boreholes and adits (tunnels) that intercept joints and fractures within the rock.

There is still however, one untapped discharge of freshwater from the Chalk aquifer, situated below Limekiln Bottom along the Seven Sisters, which is visible at low tide. It is likely to be linked to a major joint or fissure system below the dry valley. Freshwater discharges from beneath the overlying shingle beach and flows across the Wave-cut Platform, significantly deepening the seaward end of the gullies. During 1992, the then Eastbourne Water Company carried extensive borehole work to investigate this 'leakage.' It was however, never pursued as an abstraction source. Water abstraction for the public supply can exert an additional pressure on the water and wetland environments, especially during periods of drought.

With the use of powerful tractors, modern agriculture shifted sig-

Autumn ploughing taking place near Wilmington.

nificantly in the period 1970-1980 towards **Autumn Ploughing** including many of the steeper Downland slopes. During this period, this gave the South Downs the onerous distinction of having some of the highest soil erosion rates in the country. On the Downs today, operations are still dominated by intensive arable cropping, though the situation at the time of writing is rapidly changing with more Downland being put down to grass; see **Farm Support Practices** (Text Box No. 18). Conservation of the small amount of remaining wildlife-rich calcareous grassland has greatly increased in the last two decades. **Sheep Grazing** has also significantly increased on the Downs during the past 25 years from its low of the 1950's.

Text Box No. 18. Aspects of the COMMON AGRICULTURAL POLICY (CAP) reform process are seeing the expansion of grassland over arable, but conversely, livestock numbers are expected to decline. Recent changes in the farming sector and the Common Agricultural Policy have increased the trend towards managing the countryside for greater public and environmental benefit.

*Defra's **Single Payment Scheme** has replaced the previous production-related payments, with payments now related to agricultural and environmental condition. Eligibility for subsidies are having to increasingly comply with EC legislation on environmental protection and is likely to encourage the greater adoption of other land management options. The Forestry Commission's Woodland Grant Scheme provides grants for the creation of new woodlands and appropriate management of existing woodlands. **Biodiversity Action Plans (BAP's)** provide national and county-based frameworks for the protection of threatened habitats and species, although they are not currently statutory documents. BAP's are however, acknowledged in development planning documents.*

With respect to **Flint Walling**, England has probably made greater use of flint than other countries where this material occurs. When considering traditional building materials in relation to the South Downs, one's mind immediately conjures with Sussex flint barns, lichen-encrusted farm and cottage walls. This technique involved lime mortar made from locally quarried Chalk. They have been a source of inspiration for generations of artists, writers and in more recent times, photographers and film directors. Most flint structures are built of field flint - flint which has been collected from off the arable fields of the Downs.

CHAPTER 12
Ecology

The area contains a considerable array of wildlife habitats including a number that are of national and international importance. Habitats range from an extensive **Wave-cut Platform** created with the retreat of the precipitous Chalk cliffs. Stretching away either side of the river estuary are broad deposits of **Shingle** boldly demarcating the valley from the waters of the English Channel. Ribbons of **Saltmarsh** border the lower reaches of the river, behind which are to be found **Wet Meadows** with winding brackish and freshwater **Ditches** and **Ponds**. Above, on the lower Downland slopes, agriculturally improved grassland predominate, that is, land that has been ploughed and then re-seeded with more agriculturally productive grasses, though poor in terms of biodiversity.

Upon the steeper Downland slopes, remnants of the famous soft, springy Downland sward survive on the nutrient poor, shallow soils, referred to as **Chalk Grassland**. The resulting beautiful soft brown-green mantle forms one of the richest habitats for wild flowers and invertebrates in Western Europe. A semi-natural habitat, this has developed over many hundreds of years, by flocks of sheep grazing the dry, nutrient-poor grasslands that have developed on the thin soils overlying the Chalk. These thin soils resulted from the removal of the natural tree cover upon the Downs during prehistoric times. Chalk soils are inherently poor because of the properties of the main constituent of Chalk, calcium carbonate, which 'locks up' other trace elements. Pony grazing is now increasingly being brought in to safeguard selected areas in order to counter the decrease in use of the land for farm livestock grazing.

The Cuckmere valley is also at the centre of a haven in which the world's most virulent tree disease - Dutch Elm Disease, is rigorously controlled. This fungal disease that arrived on these shores some four decades ago is carried by elm bark beetles; diseased trees are promptly removed by summer-time felling. This is the only locality on earth in which large mature specimens of **English Elm**, *(Ulmus procera)* (and other elm species) may still be enjoyed. Within the area covered by this book there is in the region of some 65,000 elm trees. The local author- ites should be congratulated for their unstinting fight in the protection of this national archive.

On the eastern flank of the Cuckmere valley, stretches the two thousand acres (809 hectares) of **Friston Forest**, a Forestry Commission undertaking that commenced following the First World War, originally as a strategic timber reserve. This has endowed the area with an exten- sive, tranquil, broad-leaved forest (mainly comprised of beech), which also serves as an important water catchment area.

As one travels north from the Downs, the initial low-lying, but gen- tly undulating clay landscape, gradually gives way to a countryside increasingly consisting of small, intimate fields of pasture on sandstone ridges. These, are divided by abundant **Hedgerows** and frequent **Ancient Woodland** with its attendant spring-time spectacle of bluebells and **Shaws**, (remnants of the medieval wildwood) together with sea- sonally, fast-flowing **Streams**. Eventually, wide vistas across the High Weald and back towards the Downs are to be enjoyed; at the same time the wide sweep of Ashdown Forest with its rich assemblages of **Heathland** is waiting.

After 'exploring' this beautiful landscape, with its rich assemblage of wildlife, there is a serious threat to certain aspects of its survival – from **Climate Change**. Current levels of the two main greenhouse gases, carbon dioxide and methane, within the atmosphere are now higher than at any time in the last 650,000 years. Research shows that carbon dioxide (CO_2) is about 30% higher and methane (CH_4), is 130% high- er, than at any time in the last 650,000 years. The main sources for these changes to carbon dioxide are from the burning of fossil fuels: oil, coal, and gas. Methane, is augmented largely by the decay of rubbish and from dunging by the worlds now huge population of cattle and is twen- ty one times more powerful than CO_2 as a greenhouse gas. Before the Industrial Revolution, atmospheric concentrations of CO_2 were about 270-280 parts per million (ppm); currently they now stand at almost 380ppm, rising at about 1.5ppm annually. In 1999, it was calculated that the aviation industry contributed in the region of 3.5% of human- induced global warming. Passenger travel is now growing by 5% per year, with air freight expanding at 6% per year. Projections show avia- tion's contribution to global warming will rise by between 2.6 and 11 times by the year 2050.

During the late 20th century, the northern hemisphere has experi- enced its most widespread warming for 1,200 years. Research has taken into account, the known periods of climate variability over the last two thousand years in the northern hemisphere, those of significant warmth, AD 890 - 1170 (the so-called "Medieval Warm Period") and for the much colder period from 1580 - 1850 (the "Little Ice Age").

Plankton are the microscopic free-floating marine organisms which are vitally important to the Earth's life support systems. Phyto-plankton (or 'tiny plants'), carry out 50% of the photosynthesis on Earth. Zoo-plankton (or 'tiny animals'), form the base for the whole of the marine food web. Within the North Sea for instance, the make-up of these plankton have under gone huge changes in their composition within the last few decades. The decline of a particular species of phyto-plank-ton which say, blooms in early spring, causes fundamental changes further up the food chain. Many other small organisms feed upon this spring bloom, even timing their own emergence to match it. In turn, a domino effect takes place and in some instances, going up through the food chain to affect birds.

From the dawn of time, extinction has usually taken place at a natural, or background rate. Many scientists now believe we are now inducing the sixth mass extinction to affect life on Earth, the last being at the end of the Cretaceous Period. By comparision with the end of the Cretacious Period, extinctions today are taking place at an even faster pace. Science has described 1.75 million species, with experts estimating that there may be as many as 13 or 14 million species, nobody knows for certain. The human pillage of the natural world has been likened to 'burning down the medieval libraries of Europe, before having even bothered to catalogue their contents.' Plants and bacteria carry out photosynthesis, thus producing the oxygen we breathe; trees absorb carbon dioxide, the main greenhouse gas given off by human activities. Many species keep us alive by purifying water, fixing nitrogen, recycling nutrients and waste and by pollinating crops.

In conclusion, the consequence of increasing CO_2 and other pollutants is bringing about higher average global temperatures, leading to increases in incidences of unpredictable weather, to rising sea levels and possibly even to a runaway global heating scenario. By 2100, average global temperatures could be between 1.5 and 5.5 degrees higher than now. Initially that may not appear to be very much, but the temperature during last Ice Age was only 4-5 degrees cooler than that of the present day. With sea level having already risen by 1-2mm per year over the past century, research predicts it could rise by a total of anything up to 88cm during the course of the next century.

BIBLIOGRAPHY

Many books, articles and original papers were consulted during the writing of this book. In a scientific publication these would have been referred to in the main text at the appropriate places. However, in order to make the subject less daunting to a general audience, references are not included although an enormous debt is owed to the authors of these works. For those readers who wish to follow up on some of the subject matter dealt with in this book, a selected reading list follows:

Bristow, C.R, Mortimore, R.N. and Wood, C.J. Lithostratigraphy for Mapping the Chalk of Southern England. Proceedings of the Geologists Association, 1997, vol. 108, pages 293 – 315.

British Geological Survey. 1:50000 scale Geological Maps of England and Wales, (Solid and Drift editions), sheet numbers: 319 (Lewes) and 334 (Eastbourne).

British Geological Survey. Rockfall at Beachy Head, South Coast of Britain report.

Brunsden, D, Gardner, R, Goudie, A, Jones, D. Land Shapes. David & Charles, 1988.

Environment Agency. Cuckmere and Sussex Havens Catchment Flood Management Plan.

Environment Agency. Cuckmere Estuary Restoration Project.

Harris, C.S. Chalk of Kent.

H.M.S.O. The Wealden District. British Regional Geology Series, 1968.

Invicta Media website. http://www.theotherside.co.uk. How The Channel Was Formed.

Joint Nature Council for Conservation. Introduction To The Tertiary.

Jones, D.K.C. The Geomorphology Of The British Isles – Southeast And Southern England, Methuen, 1981.

Open University Geological Society, London Branch Archive Site. Field trip reports.

Potrsdown Hill website. http://www. bbm.me.uk/portsdown.

Rae, Alison. Chalk and Clay Landscapes; Nelson Thorne Ltd., 2001.

Rescue The Cuckmere Valley website.

Standing Conference on Problems Associated With The Coastline. River Adur, Shoreham by Sea to Beachy Head Report.

Steers, J.A., The Sea Coast; New Naturalists Series, Collins, 1962.

Surrey Museum Service website. http://www.surreymuseums.org.uk/collections/geology.

The Geological Society. The Chalk Group – A Revised Lithostratigraphy.

University College, London, School of Geological Sciences. papers on Coccoliths and Nannofossils.

University of Brighton, Applied Geology Research Unit. Chalk Cliffs.

University of Sussex, School of Biological Sciences. Darwinian Evolution – Surface Geology of Sussex.

Woolridge, S.W. & Goldring, F., The Weald; New Naturalist Series, Collins, 1972.

INDEX